THE SIMPSONS 2011 ANNUAL

For information address
Bongo Comics Group
P.O. Box 1963, Santa Monica, CA 90406-1963, USA

Published in the UK by Titan Books, a division of Titan Publishing Group Ltd,
144 Southwark St., London SE1 0UP, under licence from Bongo Entertainment, Inc and Matt Groening Productions, Inc..

FIRST EDITION: AUGUST 2010
ISBN: 9781848568341
3 5 7 9 10 8 6 4 2

Publisher: Matt Groening
Creative Director: Bill Morrison
Managing Editor: Terry Delegeane
Director of Operations: Robert Zaugh
Art Director: Nathan Kane
Art Director Special Projects: Serban Cristescu
Production Manager: Christopher Ungar
Assistant Art Director: Chia-Hsien Jasooon Ho
Production/Design: Karen Bates, Nathan Hamill, Art Villanueva
Staff Artist: Mike Rote
Administration: Ruth Waytz, Pete Benson
Legal Guardian: Susan A. Grode

Contributing Artists:
Karen Bates, John Costanza, Mike DeCarlo, Serban Cristescu, Alan Hellard,
Nathan Kane, Mike Kazaleh, James Lloyd, Bill Morrison, Vinny Navarrette, Phil Ortiz, Patrick Owsley, Mike Rote, Howard
Shum, Robert Stanley, Carlos Valenti, Art Villanueva
Contributing Writers:
James W. Bates, Chuck Dixon, Earl Kress,
Mary Trainor, Patric C. W. Verrone, Patric M. Verrone

PRINTED IN ITALY

THE SIMPSONS

ANNUAL 2011

TITAN BOOKS

6

OFF THE GRID

JAMES W. BATES
SCRIPT

PHIL ORTIZ
PENCILS

MIKE DECARLO
INKS

ROBERT STANLEY
COLORS

KAREN BATES
LETTERS

BILL MORRISON
EDITOR

AT THE BURNS MANSION...

LOOK AT ALL THAT ELECTRICITY! LIGHTS BURNING, HEATERS FIRING! ISN'T IT BEAUTIFUL?

I'D GO AS FAR AS TO SAY IT WAS ROMANTIC, SIR.

SHOW ME THE CHART AGAIN, SMITHERS.

EXCELLENT!

THIS COLD SNAP HAS REALLY FORCED YOUR CONSUMERS TO CRANK UP THEIR THERMOSTATS.

YES, AND IN THE WAKE OF THEIR GREEDY USE OF THE ENERGY I *SUPPLY*, I *DEMAND* A RAISE IN PRICES!

ALL THIS CHATTER ABOUT THE COLD HAS SENT A CHILL DOWN MY SPINE. SMITHERS, PUT ANOTHER LOG ON THE FIRE.

SIR, WOULD YOU LIKE TO BURN A LOG OF FIFTIES OR HUNDREDS?

THIS CAN'T BE RIGHT! HOW CAN THEY WANT THIS MUCH? I *WON'T* PAY IT!

BILL

I DON'T THINK WE *CAN* PAY IT.

WE CAN ALWAYS DIP INTO BART'S COLLEGE FUND.

BWAH-HA-HA-HA!!!

YOU KNOW EVERY TIME YOU MAKE THAT JOKE, MY SELF-ESTEEM DIES A LITTLE.

IT'S AWFUL THAT THEY'D BUMP UP PRICES IN THE WINTER WHEN PEOPLE NEED FUEL THE MOST.

NEXT WEEK, THERE'S A GREAT DOCUMENTARY AIRING. IT'S CALLED "PLANET ON PROBATION."

HUH, WHAT? SORRY, I FELL ASLEEP WHILE YOU WERE YAMMERING ABOUT SOME DOCUMENTARY.

YOU'LL SEE! THAT SHOW IS GOING TO EXPOSE HOW THE POWER COMPANIES MANIPULATE PRICES.

ZZZZZ!

WE HAVE TO DO SOMETHING ABOUT THESE BILLS.

WE CAN CUT OUR COSTS BY BECOMING MORE ENERGY CONSCIOUS.

CUTTING COSTS WON'T JUST HELP US, BUT IT'LL ALSO STICK IT TO THE MAN!

I LIKE THE SOUND OF THAT. WHAT DO WE HAVE TO DO?

IT'S SIMPLE...WE USE *LESS POWER*.

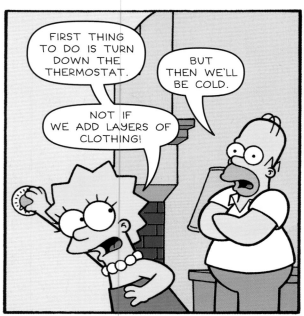

FIRST THING TO DO IS TURN DOWN THE THERMOSTAT.

BUT THEN WE'LL BE COLD.

NOT IF WE ADD LAYERS OF CLOTHING!

BUT SWEATERS DON'T COMPLIMENT MY FIGURE.

BART, SHUSH!

MMPHGGGH!

THIS SAYS THAT FOR EVERY ONE DEGREE WE LOWER THE THERMOSTAT THAT WE'LL SAVE FIVE PERCENT ON OUR HEATING BILL.

THE LATE GREAT OVERHEATED EARTH

FIVE PERCENT FOR EVERY DEGREE? I SAY WE TURN IT *ALL THE WAY OFF!*

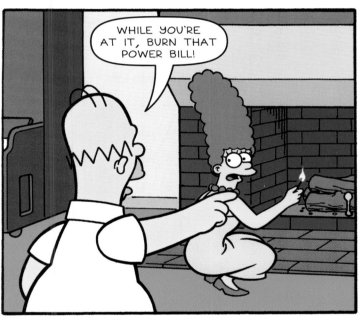

AS OF THIS MOMENT, THE SIMPSONS ARE GOING *OFF THE GRID!*

NO MORE BURNS HEAT! NO MORE BURNS ELECTRICITY! WE'RE GONNA LIVE POWER FREE AND GREEN!

I DON'T KNOW...

WE'RE GOING TO MAKE A STATEMENT!

YEAH..."HELP! WE'RE FREEZING TO DEATH!"

THIS IS A GREAT OPPORTUNITY TO SHOW EVERYONE HOW THEY CAN CONSERVE POWER AND STILL GET BY.

CLICK!

I GUESS IF WE'RE REALLY GOING TO DO THIS, WE BETTER BUNDLE UP.

WE *ARE* DOING THIS! MY RESOLVE IS STRONG!

RIGHT ON, DAD!

READING BY CANDLELIGHT! I FEEL LIKE LAURA INGALLS IN "THE LITTLE HOUSE ON THE PRAIRIE!"

THAT MUST BE NICE FOR YOU, BUT *I* FEEL LIKE A BAG OF FROZEN PEAS.

BART, I KNOW IT'S TOUGH, BUT TRY TO THINK WARM THOUGHTS.

I DON'T THINK I CAN LIVE ANOTHER MINUTE WITHOUT THE TV!

WAY TO STAY STRONG, HOMER.

HOMIE, IT'S ONLY BEEN FORTY-FIVE MINUTES.

THE LONGEST FORTY-FIVE MINUTES OF MY LIFE!

ALL ADDICTS GO THROUGH WITHDRAWAL.

I'M NOT ADDICTED TO TV. I'M COOL.

IF HOMER WAS ADDICTED, HE'D CARE THAT "THE WIDE WORLD OF WACKY MONKEYS" IS ON RIGHT NOW.

D'OH! I'M MISSING WACKY MONKEYS.

NEXT MORNING...

NO ALARM? WHAT TIME IS IT?

YOU'RE LATE FOR WORK!

I'M GONNA HAVE TO DRIVE THROUGH EVERY STOP SIGN AND RED LIGHT!

NO YOU WON'T!

I HAVE TO! IF I GET THERE TOO LATE, THE VENDING MACHINE SELLS OUT OF CINNAMON ROLLS.

YOU'RE FORGETTING SOMETHING.

MY PANTS!

THAT'S NOT ALL.

OF COURSE! A GOOD-BYE KISS!

YOU ARE FORGETTING OUR NEW ECO-FRIENDLY-POWER-INDEPENDENT LIFESTYLE. *NO DRIVING!*

⸾HUFF-PUFF-HUFF-PUFF...⸾

THAT NIGHT...

GREAT SALAD, MOM!

THIS IS ALL I COULD THINK TO MAKE WITHOUT THE OVEN.

NEXT TIME, YOU SHOULD THROW IN A FEW CAYENNE PEPPERS! THEY IMPROVE THE BODY'S BLOOD FLOW AND KEEP YOU WARM FROM THE INSIDE OUT.

YOU SAID WE SHOULD JUST THINK WARM THOUGHTS.

BART, YOU REALLY NEED TO IMPROVE YOUR ATTITUDE.

NO. I NEED HEAT.

LOOK! THE DOG AND CAT ARE SO COLD, THEY'RE SNUGGLING! THIS SILLY POWER BOYCOTT GOES AGAINST THE VERY LAWS OF NATURE!

WE MADE A DECISION AND WE HAVE TO STICK WITH IT.

IT WAS A BAD DECISION!

LOOK AT THE GENIUS WHO CAME UP WITH THE IDEA!

ZZZZZZZ!

YOUR FATHER'S A LITTLE TIRED FROM RIDING HIS BIKE TO AND FROM WORK.

LOOK AT ME! MY VIDEOGAME CONTROLLER CALLUSES ARE HEALING!

I THINK IT'S GOOD FOR YOU TO GET AWAY FROM THOSE GAMES FOR A WHILE.

HOW CAN IT BE GOOD THAT MY NINJA CAR THEFT SKILLS ARE DETERIORATING?

I KNOW YOU MISS YOUR GAMES, BUT I HAVE AN IDEA!

A *PUZZLE?*

NOT JUST A PUZZLE. A *FIVE-HUNDRED PIECE* PUZZLE!

LOOK FOR THE CORNER PIECES!

OH YEAH, THIS IS JUST AS EXCITING AS PLAYING A VIDEOGAME.

DAYS LATER...SUNDAY...

THAT WAS A VERY NICE SERMON, REVEREND LOVEJOY.

First Church of Springfield

TO EVERYTHING THERE IS A SEASON. AND IT'S THE SEASON TO TURN TURN TURN UP THE HEAT!

THANK YOU, MARGE.

YOUR HUSBAND MUST'VE MISSED THE PART ABOUT CLEANLINESS BEING NEXT TO GODLINESS.

HOMER REFUSES TO SHAVE WITHOUT HOT WATER.

I GUESS THAT GOES FOR *SHOWERING*, TOO.

BUT WHY DON'T YOU HAVE HOT WATER?

WE STOPPED USING ELECTRIC AND GAS.

BART TOLD ME THE OTHER DAY THAT YOU'VE BEEN LIVING OFF THE POWER GRID FOR A WEEK.

THE LONGEST WEEK OF MY LIFE!

I SAY "BRAVO!" YOU INSPIRED ME TO DO THE SAME THING.

INSPIRED YOU?

AND ME AS WELL!

YOU DON'T SAY?

GLAVIN! AFTER I HEARD ABOUT YOUR CAUSE, I STARTED MAKING WITH THE SOLAR PANELS AND THE WIND TURBINES. ENG-HEY!

SEE, MOM? I TOLD YOU WE WERE MAKING A REAL DIFFERENCE!

BY SHRINKING OUR CARBON FOOTPRINT, WE'RE DOING OUR PART TO SAVE THE PLANET.

IT'S A BLESSED THING. TRULY GOD'S WORK!

HEY, IT WAS *MY* IDEA!

GOOD ONE, HOMER. YOU'RE A HERO!

MMM... HERO. SUB. HOAGIE.

TURNING OFF THE POWER SOUNDS LIKE A GOOD WAY TO SHOW BURNS WHAT WE THINK OF HIM JACKING UP PRICES!

I SAY WE *ALL* GO OFF THE GRID!

YEAH!!!

SIR, DO YOU NEED MORE CAVIAR?

NO, THE BATH IS JUST FINE.

DID YOU WANT ME TO SCRUB YOUR BACK?

FOR THE UMPTEENTH TIME...NO!

I WANT TO SEE THE CHART!

WHY IS THE ARROW DROPPING LIKE A LEAD DIRIGIBLE?

USAGE IS DOWN.

POPPY-COCK! THE WEATHER OUTSIDE IS AS COLD AS ONE OF ELEANOR ROOSEVELT'S KISSES.

WORD IS THAT SOME OF YOUR COSTUMERS ARE REVOLTING AGAINST THE HIGHER RATES BY USING LESS OR NONE OF YOUR POWER!

OUTRAGEOUS!

SHOULD WE LOWER PRICES?

NEVER! WE'LL EXPLAIN TO THEM THAT WHAT THEY ARE DOING IS WRONG IN THE ONLY WAY THOSE INGRATES WILL UNDERSTAND...*AN INFOMERCIAL!*

TELEPHONE THOSE HOLLYWOOD WHIZ KIDS THAT PRODUCED MY DOCUMENTARY.

YOU SHOULD USE A SECOND CANDLE.

AT FIRST, I THOUGHT READING BY CANDLELIGHT WAS QUAINT, BUT NOW I JUST WANT TO BE ABLE TO *SEE*.

KAHLO

FIT! YOU STUPID PIECE OF...

...PUZZLE!

THUMP!

THUMP!

THUMP! THUMP! THUMP!

...IT'S TOUGH ON OUR GUYS...

BART, THOSE ARE MY GREAT WOMEN IN HISTORY BOOKS! WHAT ARE YOU DOING?

I'M SAVING THE PLANET LIKE YOU WANTED ME TO!

THOSE WOMEN ARE *GREAT* AT KEEPING THE FIRE GOING.

JOAN OF ARC

STUPID ELECTRIC FLANDERS.

MOM'S RIGHT. THE GUYS AREN'T HANDLING THIS WELL AT ALL.

LISA, HELP ME WITH THE LAUNDRY.

IT'S GOING TAKE FOREVER TO COOK PORK CHOPS OVER A FIRE IN THE BACKYARD SO I NEED YOU TO WASH THE LAUNDRY BY WHACKING THE CLOTHES WITH THESE STONES.

YOUR FATHER'S UNDERWEAR MIGHT NEED A DOUBLE WHACKING.

TV LISTINGS. HMM...THAT REMINDS ME, WHEN DOES "PLANET ON PROBATION" AIR?

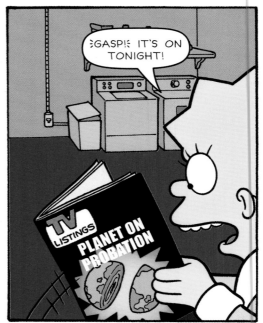

¡GASP!: IT'S ON TONIGHT!

MEANWHILE, UPSTAIRS...

DAD, WHAT ARE YOU DOING HERE?

THE NINCOMPOOPS AT THE RETIREMENT CASTLE JOINED YOUR PROTEST AND TURNED OFF THE POWER.

BUT WHAT ARE YOU DOING *HERE*?

WITH NO POWER, THERE'S NO TV. AND WITHOUT TV, ALL ANYONE THERE WANTS TO DO IS TALK!

DO YOU KNOW HOW BORING IT IS TO LISTEN TO AN OLD PERSON YAMMER? LET ME TELL YOU ABOUT IT...

I THOUGHT I HEARD SOMEONE ARRIVE. GRAMPA'S HERE.

SO IS SOMEONE ELSE.

KNOCK! KNOCK! KNOCK!

22

WHAT'S GOING ON?

HOMER, WE WE'RE WITH YOU WHEN YOU STARTED THIS BOY-COTT, BUT NOW WE NEED TO GO BACK ON THE GRID.

WHAT ABOUT STICKIN' IT TO THE MAN?

WITHOUT THE REFRIGERATION UNIT, MY SQUISHIES DO NOT SQUISH.

NO ONE WANTS TO DRINK WARM BEER, EXCEPT GROUNDS-KEEPER WILLIE.

WITHOUT LIGHTS MY "HERB" GARDEN WON'T GROW!

WHY ARE YOU HERE?

BURNS TURNED OFF OL' GIL'S POWER A MONTH AGO. I JUST TAGGED ALONG TO BE NEAR PEOPLE WHO AREN'T TRYING TO REPOSSESS SOMETHING FROM ME.

WHADDYA THINK, HOMER? IS ALL THIS PAIN AND SUFFERING WORTH IT?

WORTH IT? I DON'T KNOW. AT FIRST, I WAS MAD ABOUT MY POWER BILL, BUT THEN LISA EXPLAINED HOW WE'RE SAVING THE PLANET! WE SHOULD TO LISTEN TO HER!

UM, DAD...

...LISTEN TO ME.

THAT'S WHAT I'M TELLING THEM TO DO, HONEY.

I THINK WE SHOULD TURN THE POWER BACK ON!

WHAT?

THE END

24

What's WASHING?

Lisa **A**

Disco Stu **B**

Bart **C**

Homer **D**

HOMER

BART

LISA

DISCO STU

ANSWERS: A: LISA, B: DISCO STU, C: BART, D: HOMER

CROSSWORD

TEST YOUR SIMPSONS KNOWLEDGE RIGHT HERE!

Crossword grid answers (as filled in):
- 1 Down / Across: k e v e r / duff
- r a
- duds'n'duns / f
- s h / carl
- t o / a
- y u / n
- abe / t / d
- u e / e
- rainier / r
- g / nn / s
- r / nn / todd
- tony

ACROSS

2 The street the Simpsons live on: _ _ _ _ GREEN TERRACE (4)
4 Homer's favourite brand of beer. (4)
5 The Laundromat where the Simpsons do their washing. (4,1,4)
7 One of Homer's workmates at the Springfield Nuclear Power Plant: _ _ _ _ CARLSON (4)
8 Bart's arch-nemesis: SIDESHOW _ _ _ (3)
9 Grandpa Simpson's first name. (3)
11 The first name of Springfield's most famous action movie star: _ _ _ _ _ _ _ WOLFCASTLE (7)
13 Homer's favourite place to drink beer. (4)
14 Springfield's most notorious mobster: FAT _ _ _ _ (4)

DOWN

1 Springfield's fast-food restaurant chain owned by a certain clown. (6,6)
3 The surname of Bart's best friend. (3,6)
4 The owner of Stu's Disco. (5,3)
6 The surname of the Simpsons' next-door neighbours. (8)
10 A worker at Springfield Nuclear Power Plant and best friend of 7 ACROSS. (5)
12 The youngest child in the Flanders family. (4)

MATT GROENING

CHUCK DIXON
STORY

MIKE KAZALEH
PENCILS & INKS

NATHAN KANE
COLORS

KAREN BATES
LETTERS

BILL MORRISON
EDITOR

ONE YEAR LATER...

THE END

THE LANDFILL OF FORBIDDEN TOYS

KRUSTYCO

SO THRILL ME.

CHUCK DIXON SCRIPT | **JOHN COSTANZA** PENCILS | **HOWARD SHUM** INKS | **ROBERT STANLEY** COLORS | **KAREN BATES** LETTERS | **BILL MORRISON** EDITOR

A WHOLE *NEW* LINE OF KRUSTY-RELATED TOYS AND NOVELTIES!

YOU'RE GONNA *OWN* CHRISTMAS, KRUSTY!

LOOKS LIKE THE SAME OLD *CRAP* TO ME.

AND MY LATTE IS COLD.

HOW ABOUT THIS *KRUSTYBOT*? IT TRANSFORMS INTO A CADILLAC ESCALADE!

WELCOME TO 1983, GENIUS. WHAT *ELSE* HAVE YOU GOT?

THIS. THE *MUST-HAVE* TOY OF THE YEAR!

MATT GROENING

THIS NISCHTIK KNICK-KNACK? *THIS* IS YOUR BEST SHOT?

JUST A CHEAP ACTION FIGURE, RIGHT? BUT ADD *WATER* AND...

...STAND BY FOR SUPER-HYDRO-ACTION KRUSTY!

YEEEK!

WOW!

SPROING!

THE LITTLE IDIOTS WILL *PLOTZ* FOR THIS!

EEP?

WE'LL SELL *MILLIONS!* *BILLIONS!*

ENVIRONMENTAL PROTECTION AGENCY!

NOBODY *MOVE!*

PACK THIS STUFF UP! IT'S *ALL* TAINTED!

TAINTED?

THESE PLAYTHINGS ARE ALL ECOLOGICAL *VIOLATIONS!*

LIKE *WHAT?*

DIOXINS, CHLORIDES, ANIMAL FECES, MERCURY, LIKELIHOOD OF ELECTRICAL SHOCK, FIRE HAZARDS, ACIDS...

OOOOOH...

IT ALL BEGAN AT KRUSTYCO PLAYTHING ASSEMBLY PLANT #9 IN SHANGCHOW, CHINA."

"THE PLACE WAS A **SMORGASBORD** OF SAFETY AND HEALTH VIOLATIONS AND A DISASTER WAITING TO HAPPEN."

"LIKE THE **LEAD** PAINT THEY USED. **RADIOACTIVE** LEAD PAINT."

SEE HOW CAPITALIST CLOWN'S EYES **GLOW** WITH LAUGHTER!

"AND THAT'S JUST THE **BEGINNING** OF THE VIOLATIONS."

ENOUGH OF YOUR PRIDE! WE ARE **BEHIND** QUOTA! SPOILED AMERICAN CHILDREN DEMAND HIGHER QUANTITY!

I HEARD **THAT!**

YOUR ENTIRE **BACKSTOCK** IS TOXIC. IT WILL HAVE TO BE DISPOSED OF **IMMEDIATELY!**

EVERY TOY, CLOWN!

FEH.

AND WHERE ARE **YOU** TWO GOING?

UM...

THE NEXT DAY...

THIS IS THE ONLY WAY, KRUSTY. YOUR CHRISTMAS INVENTORY BURIED FOR A MILLION YEARS.

YOU MEAN A MILLION *BUCKS*. OY.

HEY HEY!
HEY HEY!
HEY HEY!
HEY HEY!
HEY HEY!
HEY HEY!
HEY HEY!

CREEPY.

THE LEGENDARY LANDFILL OF FORBIDDEN TOYS.

WHAT'S *THAT* MEAN?

THIS IS THE FINAL RESTING PLACE OF THE UNSOLD, THE UNSAFE, AND THE UNMARKETABLE.

LIKE "DON'T ASK, DON'T TELL" G.I. JOE.

HOW MANY TIMES HAVE *YOU* SEEN "WICKED?"

AND *ROACH FARM*.

OR SINGLE MOM MALIBU STACY.

NEW

AND ALL THE TOYS FROM THE *"TREASURE PLANET"* LICENSE.

EXACTLY.

TREASURE *WHAAA?*

NOW THE CONCRETE CONTAINMENT CAP IS POURED TO HOLD IN THE RADS AND TOXINS.

AND CRAPPY HOLIDAYS FOR *THIS* FUNNYMAN.

WELL, THAT'S THE END OF *THAT*.

I NEED A VODKA SPRITZER.

MONTHS LATER...

SNOW *BEFORE* THANKSGIVING?

COME *ON*, BABY! *ACCUMULATE!*

YOU KIDS BETTER GET OUT THERE BEFORE IT MELTS.

A FEW MORE INCHES AND THEY'LL ANNOUNCE *SCHOOL* CLOSINGS! SNOW *RULES!*

SEVERAL WEEKS AND FIVE FEET OF SNOW LATER...

IT'S SNOWING. AGAIN.

YOU MEAN, IT'S *STILL* SNOWING.

LOOKS LIKE *ANOTHER* SNOW DAY, KIDS.

WE'LL BE MAKING UP SCHOOL DAYS ALL *SUMMER*.

SNOW *SUCKS*.

...AND THERE'S MORE WHITE STUFF IN THE FORECAST...

...AS WHITE CHRISTMAS TURNS TO *BLIGHT* CHRISTMAS!

LET'S GO TO *ARNIE PIE* HIGH IN THE SKY FOR THE *TRAFFIC!*

THERE'S *NO* ACTION ON THE ROADS. MUCH LIKE YOUR *LOVE LIFE*, KENT.

ALL MAJOR HIGH-WAYS INTO SPRINGFIELD ARE *WHITED OUT!*

STATE POLICE ARE TURNING BACK *ALL* TRUCKS!

LOOKS LIKE *SOME* KIDS *AREN'T* GOING TO GET ANY TOYS THIS CHRISTMAS!

NO TOYS!

PLEASE TELL US YOU *ALREADY* WENT SHOPPING, DAD!

PLEASE!

HA HA. DO YOU KIDS THINK I'M *THAT* BIG A SCREW-UP?

MARGE! I *SCREWED* UP!

I'M SURE IT'S NOT *THAT* BAD, HOMIE.

I DIDN'T BUY THE KIDS' *GIFTS* YET!

THIS *IS* TERRIBLE!

I *KNOW!* THEIR SAD LITTLE FACES *STARING* UP AT ME ON CHRISTMAS MORNING.

WHO CAN I *BLAME* THIS ON?

WELL, THE SNOW IS AN ACT OF *GOD*.

GOD! WHY CAN'T YOU LEAVE CHRISTMAS *ALONE?*

CHRISTMAS DAY...

YAAAAAAAY!

NO...NO...

WHAT'S *THIS* SUPPOSED TO BE?

34

MERRY CHRISTMAS, KIDS!

LOOK! SANTA BROUGHT YOU A ROBOT PUPPY!

THAT'S OUR DOG WRAPPED IN FOIL.

A DOLL-HOUSE MADE FROM A LAUNDRY HAMPER?

COOKIE DOUGH ACTION FIGURES?

EW... THIS IS MADE FROM DAD'S SOCKS.

WE GOT HOSED, LIS.

THAT AFTERNOON...

...¦GRUMBLE¦... ¦GRUMBLE¦...

...¦CARP¦...

...¦GRUMBLE¦... ¦MOAN¦...

ARE ALL YOUR STOCKINGS EMPTY?

MY DAD GAVE ME HIS ROLLOVER MINUTES.

WE GOT ZILCH. ZIPPO.

NADA. ZERO.

MY PARENTS ARE DIVORCED! THIS WAS SUPPOSED TO BE MY PAY OFF!

GOD? WHY DID YOU DO THIS? THESE KIDS WEREN'T NAUGHTY. AND THIS PAST YEAR'S BEEN A PERSONAL BEST FOR ME.

MEANWHILE, OUT AT THE LANDFILL...

...THE PRESSURE FROM INSIDE HAS CAUSED STRESS FRACTURES IN THE CONCRETE.

THE HEAT FROM DEEP WITHIN THE CONTAINER MELTS THE SNOW...

...AND THE WATER REACHES THE SUPER-HYDRO-ACTION KRUSTY TOYS.

MILLIONS OF TONS OF PRESSURE BUILD UP FROM THE EXPANDING CLOWNS...

...UNTIL THE LANDFILL *BLOWS!*

KA-BOOM!

THE END

Homer Simpson presents

A GOURMET'S GUIDE TO FINE DINING

> HERE'S MY ONE AND ONLY RULE FOR MASTERING THE SCIENCE OF FINE DINING: EAT EVERY MEAL LIKE IT'S YOUR LAST MEAL. TAKE NO PRISONERS, LEAVE NO LEFTOVERS, AND TELL THAT WAITERER HE CAN HAVE YOUR FORK WHEN HE PRIES IT FROM YOUR COLD, DEAD HAND.

Know Your Finger Foods

TURKEY DRUMSTICK? — YES!

CREAMED CORN? — NO!

PORK CHOP? — YES!

SOUP? — NO!

T-BONE STEAK? — YES!

SPAGHETTI AND MEATBALLS? — HMMMM. MAYBE...

The Buffet

The all-you-can-eat buffet. Mmmmm. This is man's finest hour. It's like Custard's Last Stand and D-Day rolled into one. First, get in close to the table and hold your position. Don't load yourself down with napkins, plates, and utensils... just arm yourself with one good, all-around fork or big spoon. Stand your ground and keep shoveling. And remember, it's every man for himself.

The 7 Basic Food Groups
Homer's Golden Pyramid of Foodly Delights

Group I – FATS
Pork Chops, Pork Rinds &
Pork By-products

Group II – SALTS
Chips, Pretzels
& Margaritas

Group III – POTATOES
Smashed, Fried
& Crinkled

Group IV – SAUCES
Applesauce,
Butter & Mayo

Group V – GREASES
Pizza, Onion Rings &
Double Cheeseburgers
with Bacon

Group VI – BEERS
Bottles, Cans & Kegs

Group VII – DONUTS
Glazed, Jellied
& Sprinkled

Ideally, there will be some seepage between food groups resulting in meals that are, at once, fatty, salty, greasy, and beery in one delicious bite.

A Tip on Tipping

In olden days waiterers and waiteresses had to count on tips in order to eke out their meager existence. But now, thanks to the federally government insured guaranteed minimum wage law, waiterers and waiteresses make more money than most illegal farm workers. So, nowadays, tipping is no longer necessary. In fact, it has been my experience in fancy restaurants to have the waiterer find my tip to be downright insulting.

The Place Setting

At a formal table setting, you always get way more silverware than you need, so don't be shy about pocketing any extra knives or sporks.

EARWAX REMOVER

SPIT DISH

NOSE WIPER

FOOD BOWL

BEER

BEER CHASER

AFTER DINNER BEER

STEAK FORK

PORK FORK

DORK FORK

SPILL CATCHER

STABBING TOOL

SOUVENIR SPOON

MASHED POTATO SPOON

Lisa Simpson in READING NIGHT

IS EVERYBODY READY FOR MY "FAMILY READING NIGHT"?

WALT WHITMAN

I AM! I HAVE AN *EXCITING* AGATHA CHRISTIE NOVEL!

D'OH! I FORGOT!

AGATHA CHRISTIE MURDER ON...

DAD!

IT'S OKAY! I'LL READ MY DUFF BEER BOTTLE LABEL!

"CONTAINS ONLY THE FINEST HOPS."

HEE, HEE! *HOPS*...WHAT A SENSE OF HUMOR THEY HAVE!

I'M READING "THE CAT WEARS A HAT"!

BART! THAT BOOK IS ONLY AT THE *FIRST GRADE* READING LEVEL!

EARL KRESS
STORY

JAMES LLOYD
PENCILS

PATRICK OWSLEY
INKS

ART VILLANUEVA
COLORS

KAREN BATES
LETTERS

BILL MORRISON
EDITOR

:GROAN: I DIDN'T THINK IT HAD *ANY* WORDS IN IT! I WAS JUST GONNA LOOK AT THE *PICTURES*!

GRRR!! WOULD YOU ALL RATHER *WATCH TV*?

YES!!

LATER...

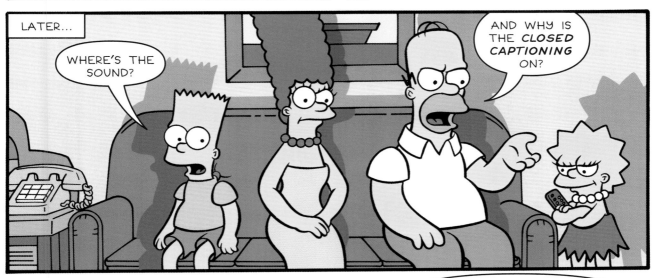

WHERE'S THE SOUND?

AND WHY IS THE *CLOSED CAPTIONING* ON?

HEY! YOU'RE MAKING US *READ TV!* WHAT A GYP!

GIVE ME THAT REMOTE!

REACH F SKY, PA

THE VIEWS OF LISA SIMPSON ARE HER OWN, AND DO NOT NECESSARILY REFLECT THOSE OF KRUSTILU STUDIOS, WHO WOULD LIKE TO REMIND YOU THAT THERE'S STILL *PLENTY* TO WATCH ON TELEVISION!

GIVE A HOOT! WATCH MY SHOW!

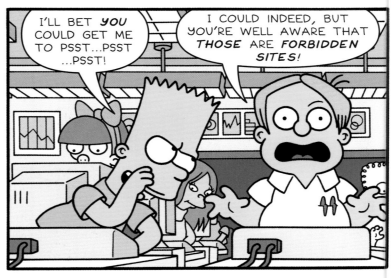

EARL KRESS
STORY

JAMES LLOYD
PENCILS

MIKE ROTE
INKS

ART VILLANUEVA
COLORS

KAREN BATES
LETTERS

BILL MORRISON
EDITOR

MARGE'S LIST OF MILDLY DISAPPROVED OF WORDS AND PHRASES

OBJECTS IN MIRROR ARE CLOSER THAN THEY APPEAR

SLIPSHOD

TOMATO

YOUR MILEAGE MAY VARY

DELINQUENT

PLEASE WAIT TO BE SEATED

PRICES SUBJECT TO CHANGE WITHOUT NOTICE

MATURE AUDIENCES ONLY

EXACT CHANGE ONLY

VIEWER DISCRETION ADVISED

DRY CLEAN ONLY

KID-VID

DO NOT REMOVE UNDER PENALTY OF LAW

ONE SIZE FITS ALL

WRONG WAY! STOP! SEVERE TIRE DAMAGE!

JUST HEAT AND SERVE

COMIC MISCHIEF

CRUDE HUMOR

MAY CONTAIN AGGRESSIVE CONFLICT AND/OR BLOODLESS DISMEMBERMENT

HOOCHIE, COOCHIE, TART OR FLOOZY

DRAG AND DROP

WENCH, SKEEZER, SKANK, OR BIMBO

BLOOD AND/OR GORE

BROAD, DAME, SKIRT OR REFRIGERATE AFTER OPENING

MALADJUSTED

SLAPDASH

BELLYACHE

CARTOON VIOLENCE

BALL AND CHAIN

LATCHKEY KIDS

EMPTY CALORIES

HAND WASH, DRIP DRY

MATT GROENING

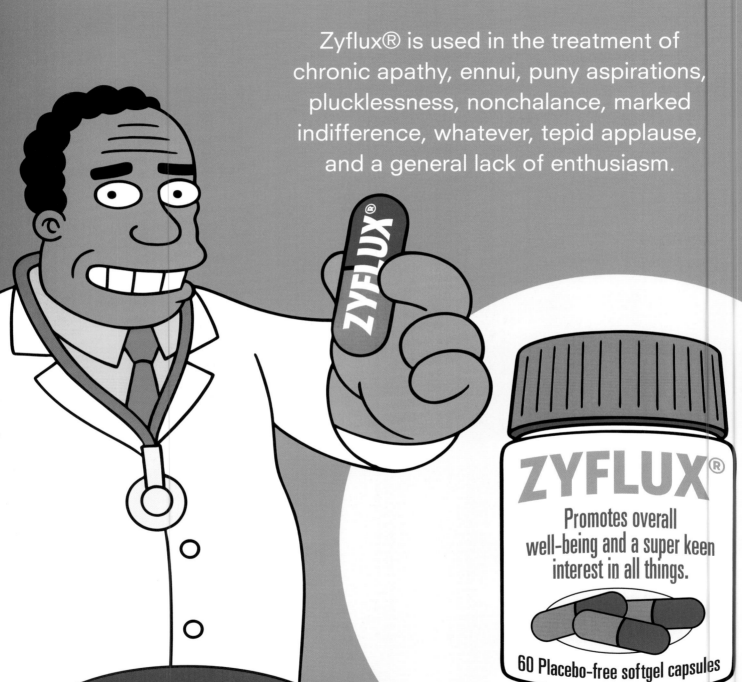

BUSY BEE PUZZLES!

who BEE these?

Four Springfield residents are surrounded by bees! But can you tell who they are?

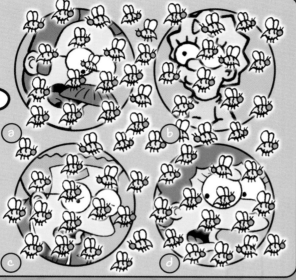

Count the spots!

HOMER WAS SAVAGELY STUNG BY A SWARM OF BEES. HOW MANY SPOTS CAN YOU COUNT ON HOMER IN THIS PICTURE?

Mrs. Hoover's BEE FACTS!

Bee clever!

- Bees have been making honey for around 150 million years!
- Bees have got five eyes.
- Bees can't recognise the colour red.
- A single hive contains about 40-45,000 bees.
- Worker bees live for only 28 to 35 days!
- A hive's temperature is about 93 degrees!
- Bees never sleep…

SPOT THE DIFFERENCE

Can you spot the five differences between these pictures?

Duff BEER INDUSTRIAL SIZE DRUMS

Bart's Cool BEE FACT!

THE BUMBLEBEE USES 21 MUSCLES TO STING! AYE, CARUMBA!

Answers: WHO BEE THESE? A: Ned! B: Maggie! C: Smithers! D: Marge! COUNT THE SPOTS: There are NO spots on Homer – they are all bee stings! SPOT THE DIFFERENCE: 1: Poster added to fence! 2: Burns bee appears! Lisa's expression changes! Label changes! Homer's face changes!

OH, PLOW, WHERE ART THOU?

I WONDER WHAT HAPPENED TO THAT PLOW.

FOR SALE

EXCUSE ME, BUT IS THIS THE SAME MR. PLOW SNOW PLOW MADE BY KOMATSU MOTORS, AS SEEN IN THE CHANNEL 92 COMMERCIAL AT 3:17 AM?

GEE, WELL, YEAH...YOU KNOW, I THINK IT IS.

FOR LE

THEN I WOULD LIKE TO PURCHASE IT. MIGHT I INQUIRE AS TO THE PRICE OF THIS FAIR-TO-POOR CONDITION ITEM?

YOU KNOW.. IT'S LIKE I WAS TELLING ANOTHER YOUNG COUPLE WHO WERE INTERESTED IN IT, YOU JUST CAN'T PUT A PRICE ON A BABY LIKE THIS.

FOR SALE

I'M SORRY, BUT YOU HAVE MISTAKEN ME FOR SOMEONE WHO DICKERS.

AW C'MON, GIVE OL' GIL ANOTHER CHANCE FOR A GIVE 'N' TAKE.

ARE YOU DEAF AS WELL AS DUMB?

I SHOULDN'T BE TELLING YOU THIS, BUT I DON'T WORK HERE. THE MANAGER JUST LETS ME SLEEP IN THE CARS.

THEN WILL YOU TAKE $100?

SOLD!

HEY, SLIM, I NEED THAT PLOW FOR A SKETCH. HOW MUCH YOU WANT FOR IT?

A MINT CONDITION ITEM LIKE THIS WITH CHOICE OF MYLAR BAG OR ACRYLIC DISPLAY CASE REQUIRES CHECKING THE ONLINE PRICE GUIDE.

I'M NOT HERE TO HAGGLE, FAT BOY. TEENY, GIVE HIM A THOUSAND SAMOLIANS.

SOLD!

WHY, KRUSTY, WHAT ARE YOU DOING IN THAT SNOWPLOW?

THERE'S NO BUSINESS LIKE SNOW BUSINESS...

THAT SKETCH STUNK ON ICE! DONATE THIS JUNK PILE TO SOME CHARITY FOR THE TAX WRITEOFF. TELL 'EM IT'S WORTH TWO THOUSAND BUCKS!

A WEEK LATER...

HMMM. I SUPPOSE WE *COULD* MELT IT DOWN AND SELL THE SCRAP METAL TO THE CATHOLICS FOR CRUCIFIXES.

YES, IT WAS JUST STOLEN. AND IT WAS INSURED FOR FIVE THOUSAND DOLLARS!

HEH HEH. LIKE STEALING CANDY FROM A BABY.

TEN GRAND? THAT'S MORE THAN YOU PAID FOR THAT FRINGE TOP SURREY I RIPPED OFF THOSE AMISH SUCKERS.

WHAT CAN I SAY? ELEMENTARY SCHOOL CUSTODIAL STAFFERS PULL DOWN SEVEN FIGURES A YEAR AND WE CAN'T SPEND IT FAST ENOUGH.

IT'S HALF PAST MONDAY MORNING. I BETTER GET HOME BEFORE I FORGET WHERE IT IS.

I'M GONNA HAVE TO CITE YOU FOR DRIVING 90 MILES AN HOUR AGAINST TRAFFIC ON TOP OF THE MEDIAN STRIP BACKWARDS WITH A BROKEN TAIL LIGHT IN A SNOW PLOW.

WHOA. I DID ALL THAT IN A SNOW PLOW? ARE YOU SURE I'M ME?

DADDY, CAN I PLAY IN THE IMPOUND LOT?

SURE, SON. LET'S SEE, ALL THOSE FINES ADD UP TO OVER $20,000 TO GET THAT PLOW BACK. KA-CHING!

55

THE TRANSCENDENTALISTS AMONG THE MEN THOUGHT IT WAS A METAPHORIC EMBODIMENT OF THEIR SOUL, WHILE THE ROMANTICISTS FOUND IT TO BE AN EPIC ALLEGORY OF OBSESSION.

IT'S A SNOW PLOW. I'LL GIVE YOU $100 FOR IT.

SOLD!

HELLO, HERMAN, WHAT'S NEW?

JUST GOT AN ITEM IN WHICH I THINK YOU MIGHT HAVE SOME INTEREST.

WORLD WAR II VINTAGE KOMATSU SNOW PLOW

I KNOW THAT PLOW! IT CAN'T BE.

ABE? YOU OKAY?

DON'T WORRY, MEN. YOU'LL BE SAFE HERE BEHIND THIS SNOW BANK WHILE I GO GET HELP.

MOE PROBLEMS MOE PUZZLES

SZYSLAK SEARCH

Can you find these 10 Moe-related words in this Moe-centric wordsearch? Answers appear horizontally, vertically, diagonally, or backwards!

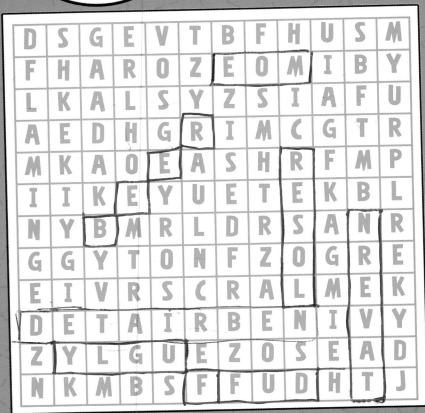

D	S	G	E	V	T	B	F	H	U	S	M
F	H	A	R	O	Z	E	O	M	I	B	Y
L	K	A	L	S	Y	Z	S	I	A	F	U
A	E	D	H	G	R	I	M	C	G	T	R
M	K	A	O	E	A	S	H	R	F	M	P
I	I	K	E	Y	U	E	T	E	K	B	L
N	Y	B	M	R	L	D	R	S	A	N	R
G	G	Y	T	O	N	F	Z	O	G	R	E
E	I	V	R	S	C	R	A	L	M	E	K
D	E	T	A	I	R	B	E	N	I	V	V
Z	Y	L	G	U	E	Z	O	S	E	A	D
N	K	M	B	S	F	F	U	D	H	T	J

MOE TAVERN **LOSER** UGLY

DUFF **BEER** INEBRIATED

FLAMING

BACHELOR **SZYSLAK**

NAME THAT GUY?

Here is the name of a famous Simpsons character, but we've jumbled it up!
Can you figure out who it is?

LAZY SMOKES

SPOT THE DIFFERENCE!

There are FIVE differences between these two pictures. Can you spot them?

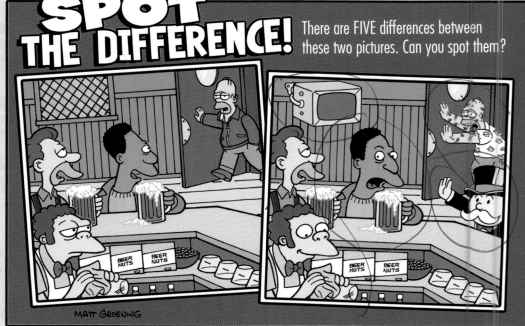

MATT GROENING

58

PATRIC M. VERRONE
SCRIPT

MIKE KAZALEH
PENCILS & INKS

ALAN HELLARD
COLORS

KAREN BATES
LETTERS

BILL MORRISON
EDITOR

WHEN OUT OF OUR BED
SHE JUMPED UP LIKE A FLEA, YELLING...

HOMER, YOU MUST PUT THE GIFTS BY THE TREE!

THE PRESENTS!

I GASPED, WITH A SLAP TO MY HEAD,
THAT GAVE ME TO KNOW
I HAD SOMETHING TO DREAD.

I'D LEFT THEM WITH GRAMPA,
WHO GAVE ME A HASSLE
WHILE MEETING HIM AT
THE RETIREMENT CASTLE.
THEN WE STOPPED OFF AT MOE'S,
AND THE REST WAS A BLUR.
NOW MY BRAIN COULDN'T TELL ME
WHERE ALL THE GIFTS WERE.

AWAY TO THE KITCHEN
I FLEW IN A PUFF,
TORE OPEN THE ICE BOX
AND THREW BACK A DUFF,

NEW PRESENTS I NEEDED
TO FIND WITH GREAT SPEED
LIKE, FOR LISA, THE PHONE BOOK...

'CAUSE SHE LIKES TO READ.

LITTLE MAGGIE WON'T MIND
IF SHE GETS THE DOG'S BOWL.
AND BART, HE DESERVES
A BIG FAT LUMP OF COAL.
BUT MARGE WON'T BE EASY
TO FOOL WITH THIS TRICK...

THEN IT DAWNED ON ME...

I COULD DRESS UP AS ST. NICK!

AN OLD SANTA SUIT'S IN THE BACK OF MY CLOSET: I'D RENTED IT, KEPT IT, AND LOST THE DEPOSIT.

PARCHINTZY
MONOTONY
SCRAMBLE

IF "SANTA" SHOWS UP WITH THESE GIFTS THERE'LL BE GLEE. IT WORKED FOR THE GRINCH, SO HOW HARD COULD IT BE?

WHILE HATCHING MY PLAN THERE AROSE SUCH A CLATTER MUCH WORSE THAN THE CAT IN THE CRAWL'S PITTER PATTER.

I WENT TO THE BOY'S ROOM TO TAKE HIM APART. I PRACTICED MY ENTRANCE...

WHY YOU LITTLE-- BART!

BUT THE SOUND WASN'T THE CAT'S NOR WAS IT THE BOY'S. SOME JERK ON MY ROOF WAS THE CAUSE OF THIS NOISE.

65

HAVE A BLAST
WITH THESE GREAT SIMPSONS BOOKS!

ISBN: 9781852865979

ISBN: 9781852866693

ISBN: 9781852867270

ISBN: 9781852867645

ISBN: 9781852868062

ISBN: 9781852869557

ISBN: 9781840230581

ISBN: 9781840231519

ISBN: 9781840234039

ISBN: 9781840235920

ISBN: 9781840237900

ISBN: 9781845760106

ISBN: 9781845762285

ISBN: 9781845764104

ISBN: 9781845767518

ISBN: 9781848562271

ISBN: 9781852868208

ISBN: 9781848565197

WWW.TITANBOOKS.COM

ISBN: 9781840234251

ISBN: 9781840236545

ISBN: 9781840238464

ISBN: 9781845760571

ISBN: 9781845763046

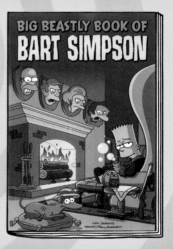

ISBN: 9781845764111

ISBN: 9781845767525

ISBN: 9781848562288

ISBN: 9781848567504

THERE'S MORE FUN INSIDE THESE GREAT ANNUALS!

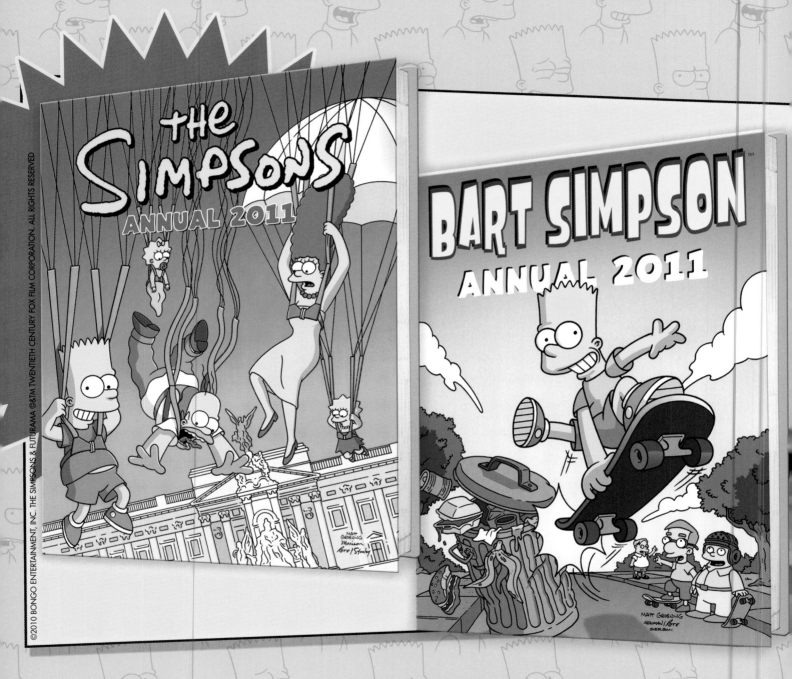

AVAILABLE NOW!

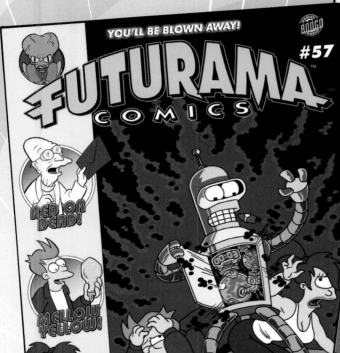
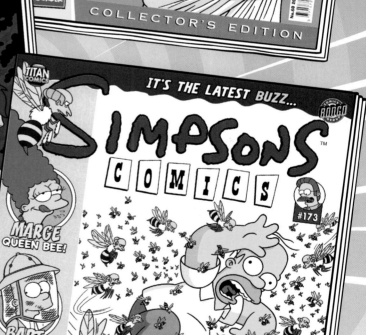